BIG
IDEAS

Linking Food, Culture, Health, and the Environment

Center for Ecoliteracy

Foreword by Michael Pollan

Learning in the Real World®

Center for Ecoliteracy
2528 San Pablo Avenue
Berkeley, CA 94702

For more information about this book, email info@ecoliteracy.org or visit www.ecoliteracy.org.

The Center for Ecoliteracy is dedicated to education for sustainable living and is a pioneer in providing tools, ideas, and support for combining hands-on experience in the natural world with curricular innovation in K–12 education.

Learning in the Real World is a publishing imprint of the Center for Ecoliteracy, a not-for-profit, tax-exempt organization. Created in 1997, Learning in the Real World publishes stories of school communities and the ecological, or systemic, understanding that informs their work.

Photo credits: Center for Ecoliteracy, Rubberball (children), Brand X (insects), Digital Vision (vegetables), istockphoto: fortune cookie/eyewave; seedling/ideeone; tortillas/Juanmonino; apples/DOConnell; sushi/Vasko; eggs/richcano; bread/motimeiri

This book was printed on paper made from 100% post consumer waste.

ISBN 978-0-9818409-0-1

WE DEDICATE THIS BOOK

to the pioneering educators who breathe life into education
for sustainable communities.

Acknowledgments

This publication was made possible through a generous grant from Nancy G. Schaub, and we offer our heartfelt thanks to Nancy for her inspiration and support.

We thank our board of directors, whose commitment to education for sustainable living has affected teachers, students, and communities nationwide: Zenobia Barlow, Peter K. Buckley, Fritjof Capra, David W. Orr, Nancy G. Schaub, and Wendy Williams.

We gratefully acknowledge Carolie Sly, Ph.D., Center for Ecoliteracy education specialist and Big Ideas project director. We also thank Leslie Comnes, lead writer and education consultant; Karen Brown, Center for Ecoliteracy creative director and designer of this publication; Dan Benesch, production consultant, and Margo Crabtree, science education consultant (and author of the big idea that sparked this book).

Thanks to Center for Ecoliteracy staff, including Zenobia Barlow, executive director; Jim Koulias, deputy director; Lisa Bennett, communications director; and Carol Denney, office assistant, for their support.

Finally, we thank our Rethinking School Lunch and Food Systems Project funders: Arkay Foundation, S. D. Bechtel, Jr. Foundation, Peter K. Buckley Fund at the Center for Ecoliteracy, The California Endowment, California Nutrition Network, Cindy Daniel, Columbia Foundation, Gellert Foundation, Greenville Foundation,

Clarence E. Heller Charitable Foundation, J. Heller Foundation, Michele Heller, Roy A. Hunt Foundation, W. K. Kellogg Foundation, Lopez Community Trust, Patricia Miriam Low Fund at the San Francisco Foundation, Nuevo Potrero Fund, Rose Foundation, Schneider Family Foundation, Janine Saperstein, Nancy G. Schaub, Small Planet Fund, Tides Foundation, United States Department of Agriculture, and Urban Village.

Key Concepts

The key concepts were reprinted from *Benchmarks for Science Literacy* (AAAS, 1993) with permission from Project 2061, on behalf of the American Association for the Advancement of Science, Washington, DC.

BIG
IDEAS

Linking Food, Culture, Health, and the Environment

Center for Ecoliteracy

Foreword by Michael Pollan

CONTENTS

FOREWORD BY MICHAEL POLLAN

IF WE ALL UNDERSTOOD that how and what we eat determines to a great extent the use we make of the world and what is to become of it, we would eat with a fuller consciousness of all that is at stake. This publication provides K–12 educators with a foundation for teaching students about food and food production, and for using this knowledge to understand the ecology of the natural world and humans' connections to it.

As a culture we seem to have arrived at a place where whatever native wisdom we may once have possessed about eating has been replaced with confusion, anxiety, and the urge to get through a meal as quickly as possible. A hallmark of the Western diet is that it is fast, cheap, and easy. Americans spend less than 10 percent of their income on food; they also spend less than a half hour a day preparing meals and little more than an hour enjoying them.

A country with a stable culture of food would not confuse protein bars and food supplements with meals or breakfast cereals with medicines. It probably would not eat a fifth of its meals in cars or feed fully a third of its children at a fast-food outlet every day. And it surely would not be nearly so fat. In the absence of such a culture, the ideas in this book can help children acquire the awareness they will need in order to reverse these trends.

Daily, our eating turns nature into culture, transforming the body of the world into our bodies and minds. Through the eyes of the cook or the gardener or the farmer who grew it, food reveals itself for what it is: no mere thing but a web of relationships among a great many living beings, some of them human, some not, but each of them dependent on the others, and all of them ultimately rooted in soil and nourished by sunlight. I'm thinking of the relationship between the plants and the soil, between the grower and the plants and animals he or she tends, between the cook and the growers who supply the ingredients, and between the cook and the people who will soon come to the table to enjoy the meal. It is a large community to nourish and be nourished by.

THIS PUBLICATION offers teachers guidance for helping students recognize their place as members of that community and a conceptual framework for using the enjoyment of food as a starting point for understanding the web of ecological relationships. It provides a basis for addressing the health and environmental problems that arise when we oversimplify nature's complexities at both the growing and the eating ends of our food chain.

The way we eat represents our most profound engagement with the natural world. It can also be the occasion for deepening our appreciation of that engagement, for the benefit of the natural world and our relationship with it.

BIG IDEAS

THE BIG IDEAS presented here provide a conceptual framework for an integrated curriculum linking food, culture, health, and the environment. They represent one component of the Center for Ecoliteracy's Rethinking School Lunch project, which helps school communities examine the health and environmental impacts of our food choices.

What we choose to put on our plate—both as individuals and as a society—has far-reaching effects. Making informed choices about our food means considering:

- where our **food** comes from and how it is produced,
- how **culture** shapes our choices and our behavior,
- the relationship between our food and our **health**, and
- the links between our food and the **environment**.

Organized around the themes of **Food, Culture, Health, and Environment**, the Big Ideas presented here help students and educators explore food systems and food choices from these four perspectives.

These specific Big Ideas were inspired by the work of the American Association for the Advancement of Science (AAAS) Project 2061, including the AAAS *Atlas of Science Literacy*. In addition to **Key Concepts** drawn from the AAAS *Benchmarks for Science Literacy*, you will find examples of **Essential Questions** that can be used to engage students and stimulate their interest in food, culture, health, and the environment. You will also find **Sample Activities** to help students explore each Big Idea.

We invite you to use these Big Ideas to lead your students in an investigation of this vital topic—food. Not only do these ideas span content areas, they can inspire learning about food in the classroom and beyond. Let them guide you as you develop learning activities for your classroom, school garden, kitchen classroom, or lunchroom.

K-2

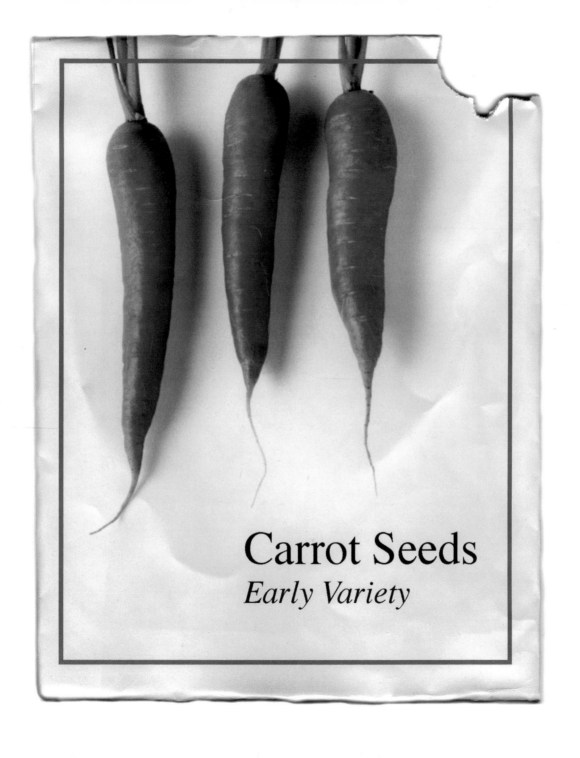

Carrot Seeds

Early Variety

FOOD

FOOD IS ESSENTIAL FOR OUR SURVIVAL. Yet most people never see food before it gets to the grocery store, and primary-aged children may have only vague ideas about where their food comes from. Looking at the food we eat and learning where it comes from are important first steps for exploring the impacts of our food choices on society and the environment.

PRODUCING FOOD

Big Idea

The food we eat comes from plants or animals, most of which are raised on farms or in gardens.

Essential Questions

What do we eat as food and where does it come from?

What do farm plants and animals need to survive and thrive?

What happens to food between the farm and your plate?

Key Concepts

- Although the food on your plate may not look like a plant or an animal, all food is made of plants or produced by animals.

- Most food comes from farms, either directly as crops or as the animals that eat the crops. (AAAS Benchmark 8A/1)

- To grow well, plants need enough warmth, light, and water. Crops also must be protected from weeds and pests that can harm them. (AAAS Benchmark 8A/1)

- Animals eat plants or other animals for food and may also use plants for shelter and nesting. (AAAS Benchmark 5D/1)

- Machines improve what people get from crops by helping in planting and harvesting. (AAAS Benchmark 8A/4)

Sample Activities

- Read a story, such as *Apple Farmer Annie* by Monica Wellington, about life on a farm or about what happens to food between the farm and the store.

- Watch plants grow from seed to edible mature plants, and help students make the connections among growing food, harvesting, and eating. Radish, leaf lettuce, or bean seeds can be grown in paper cups in the classroom or in a school garden. Students can write and draw pictures about caring for garden plants.

- Provide students with hands-on experiences preparing food from plants or plant parts, such as making applesauce from apples or strawberry jam from strawberries.

- Visit a farmer's market or local dairy, and talk to the farmers about the needs of the plants or animals they raise.

- Take a walk in the school yard or garden to look for plants that are being eaten by other animals, or read a story, such as Beatrix Potter's *The Tale of Peter Rabbit*. Discuss ways to protect plants from other animals so that people can eat the food.

- Bring in a variety of garden tools—trowels, shovels, hoes, and rakes, for example. Give students practice using them, and talk about how tools and machines help people grow food.

- Have students illustrate from farm to plate the journey of a food item served in the lunchroom. You might use a book, such as *From Cow to Ice Cream* by Bertram Knight, as a starting point.

CULTURE

FOOD IS MUCH MORE THAN JUST NOURISHMENT.
It is also a reflection of our individual tastes as well as our culture, traditions, and life situation. By identifying the food choices and eating habits of themselves and of those around them, students can begin to recognize factors involved in making healthful food choices.

UNDERSTANDING BEHAVIOR

Big Idea

People have different tastes in food.

Essential Questions

What foods do different families prefer to eat?

What customs and rules do families have about food and eating?

How are people's food choices alike and how are they different?

What are ways we learn about food from others?

Key Concepts

- People are alike in many ways and different in many ways.
  (AAAS Benchmark 7A/1)

- The way people act is often influenced by the groups to which they
  belong. (AAAS Benchmark 7B/2)

- People can learn from each other by telling and listening, showing
  and watching, and imitating what others do. (AAAS Benchmark 6D/3)

Sample Activities

- Invite students to imagine what they would choose if they could have anything they wanted for breakfast (or dinner) on their birthday or other special day. Give students paper plates and ask them to draw a picture of their ideal meal on them. Help them write short sentences describing their meal.

- Help the class select six favorite fruits, and create a graph showing the number of students who prefer each fruit. Make similar graphs for vegetables, grains, and meats and beans. Invite your school's food service manager to talk about how this information can be used to plan school lunches.

- Make a class bulletin board of rituals and rules that families have for meals and food (such as words of thanks, washing hands before eating, special foods for holidays, and so on).

- Read and discuss a story that deals with various food customs, such as *How My Parents Learned to Eat* by Ina Friedman or *Yoko* by Rosemary Wells. How are people's food customs alike, and how do they differ?

- Plant an assortment of herbs, either outdoors in the garden or indoors in pots, and for each herb explore recipes, traditions, and uses in different cultures.

- Invite parents or other community members to introduce foods from other countries for students to try. You might focus on one food category, such as grain products, with samples of roti, pita, rice, couscous, tortillas, and so on.

- Create a class cookbook of favorite family recipes, and discuss ways people learn from others about what and how to cook.

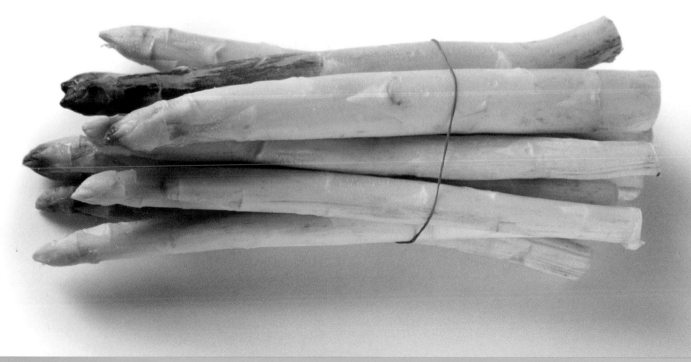

HEALTH

AS A SPECIES, HUMANS ARE QUITE CURIOUS about themselves. For young students, this innate curiosity includes questions about their own bodies and what they need to move and function. By building on this curiosity, students can explore the concept that certain foods are good for a healthy body as they start to consider the relationships among food, movement, and health.

MAINTAINING HEALTH

Big Idea

What we eat and the way we use our bodies can affect our health.

Essential Questions

What does it mean to be healthy?

What can I do to stay healthy?

What do people do that can be unhealthy?

What kinds of foods help people grow and have healthy bodies?

Key Concepts

- Eating a variety of foods and getting enough exercise and rest help people stay healthy. (AAAS Benchmark 6E/1)

- Some things people take into their bodies from the environment can harm them. (AAAS Benchmark 6E/1)

- Healthy eating habits and an active lifestyle help reduce the risk of disease.

Sample Activities

- Have students draw pictures of a healthy person, and then brainstorm words to describe someone who is healthy.

- Create a bulletin board of different ways people move their bodies. Talk about how movement and exercise are important for healthy bodies.

- Read a book on the topic of healthful eating, such as *Gregory the Terrible Eater* by Mitchell Sharmat or *Eating the Alphabet* by Lois Elhert. Make a list of healthful foods.

- Make a class chart with the headings "Fruits," "Vegetables," "Milk," "Grains," and "Meat/Beans." Cut out pictures of food from magazines, and tape them underneath the appropriate heading. Find food items that fit into each category from the school lunch menu.

- Explore balanced meals, which include foods from various food groups. Use pictures of food from magazines to create examples of different meals. Which ones are balanced and healthy? What could we do to make an unhealthy meal healthier?

- Experience the tastiness of fresh, healthful vegetables by growing them as a class. Plant radish, cherry tomato, cucumber, or sugar snap pea seeds in the garden or in pots. Water and watch the vegetables grow, and harvest them when they are ripe.

- Compile a recipe box of healthful snacks that children can prepare themselves, such as carrot sticks and peanut butter. Make copies of recipes so students can make them at home.

- Help students keep a simple picture diary of the foods they eat and the activities they participate in.

- Write a story or draw pictures of things that people should avoid putting in their bodies.

ENVIRONMENT

WHY DO PEOPLE EAT? Like all living things, we need food to stay alive. All animals—including people—take in plants or other animals for food. Plants, on the other hand, are able to create their own food using sunlight. By exploring this basic need for food, students can begin to see how their food connects them to other living things and to their environment.

SUSTAINING LIFE

Big Idea

Living things need some kind of food to live.

Essential Questions

What do plants and animals need to stay alive?

How do various plants and animals obtain their food?

What plants and animals do people eat for food?

Key Concepts

- Most living things need water, food, and air. (AAAS Benchmark 5C/1)

- Plants and animals both need to take in water, and animals need to take in food. In addition, plants need light. (AAAS Benchmark 5E/1)

- Animals eat plants or other animals for food. (AAAS Benchmark 5D/1)

Sample Activities

- On the board, list things that plants need to stay alive. Repeat for humans and for other animals. Circle the things that are on all three lists.

- Make simple bird feeders by spreading pinecones with peanut butter or suet and rolling them in birdseed. Place the feeders outside the class window, and see what kinds of birds they attract. How do the birds eat the seeds?

- Explore how sunlight affects plants: place marigold or zinnia seeds in small pots or egg cartons, and put some containers next to a sunny window and others in the dark. Compare the plants' growth and appearance. Afterward, transplant them in the garden to provide nectar for butterflies and seeds for finches and sparrows.

- Collect and record a class list of foods that students eat in a day or a week. How many different kinds of plants are on the list?

- Bring in pictures of a variety of foods, and have students identify their sources. For example, jelly comes from grapes, cheese from cows, and bread from wheat. Which sources are animals and which are plants? Is there any source that is neither animal nor plant?

- Read a picture book describing food chains, such as *The Magic School Bus Gets Eaten: A Book About Food Chains* by Pat Relf, or *Who Eats What? Food Chains and Food Webs* by Patricia Lauber.

- Make paper chains representing simple food chains to reinforce the idea that plants need sunlight to grow, some animals eat plants, and other animals eat animals. For example: Sun→Grass→Cow→Person.

- Find evidence that animals live and eat in the garden or school yard. You might find chewed leaves or fruits, nipped stems, or slimy snail trails.

3-5

FOOD

MOST OF THE PLANTS AND ANIMALS we eat are grown or raised on a farm. Once a fairly simple process, getting food from the farm to the consumer now involves a complex system that includes many different jobs, steps, and resources. Learning about the people and the effort necessary to bring food to the table is essential for understanding the impacts of our food choices.

PRODUCING FOOD

Big Idea

Producing food for our society requires many people and lots of work in planting, growing, harvesting, transporting, and processing crops, and in raising animals for eggs, milk, and meat.

Essential Questions

How do climate, soil, and other conditions affect the ability of crops and animals to thrive?

How has farming changed over time in our community and beyond?

What people, tasks, steps, and resources are required to produce food and bring it to the table?

Key Concepts

- Many people work to bring our food from the farm to our tables.

- The kinds of crops that can grow in an area depend on the climate and soil. Irrigation and fertilizers can help crops grow in places where there is too little water or the soil is poor. (AAAS Benchmark 8A/1)

- Heating, salting, smoking, drying, cooling, and airtight packaging make it possible for food to be stored for long intervals before being used. (AAAS Benchmark 8A/3)

- Modern technology has increased the efficiency of agriculture, so that fewer people are needed to work on farms than ever before. (AAAS Benchmark 8A/4)

- Much of the food eaten by Americans comes from other parts of the country and the world. (AAAS Benchmark 8A/5)

Sample Activities

- Read a story about the lives of farmers in earlier times, such as *Little House on the Prairie* by Laura Ingalls Wilder. How has farming changed and how is it the same?

- Start a photo album or scrapbook of the jobs of people involved in bringing food to the table—such as farmer, trucker, grocer, butcher, and so on. Students can look for pictures in magazines or on the Internet, and then label and add them to the album.

- Read the labels of a variety of seed packets to find out whether they are suitable for your area. Compare the information against a map showing the plant hardiness zones in your region.

- Learn about foods native to your area and, if possible, prepare a dish based on one of these ingredients—such as wild greens, cattail roots, or blueberries. Local Native American organizations or native plant societies may be helpful resources.

- Cut out pictures of food from grocery ads, and have students sort them by the environments the crops or animals grow in. Include some wild species, such as wild mushrooms or salmon.

- Grow edible plants, either in the school garden or in pots placed near a sunny window. Herbs, spinach, and leaf lettuce are good choices to try indoors from seed. Help students diagram all the steps and resources involved—from selecting appropriate seeds to determining when to harvest the plants.

- Do a taste test of fresh, dried, canned, and frozen peas (or other vegetable or fruit). Why do people preserve food? What other ways do people preserve food?

- Take students to visit a local farm, dairy, farmer's market, processing plant, grain elevator, or grocery store to learn firsthand about the steps and the people involved in bringing food from farm to table.

- Interview your school's food service director to find out the sources of some of the ingredients in the school lunch.

CULTURE

WE IDENTIFY OURSELVES THROUGH OUR FOOD and food habits. How we prepare and eat food, what we eat, and when we eat it are all influenced by culture, social customs, and economic factors. By exploring food and culture through the lens of family traditions, students build an understanding of customs that have developed around food and food preparation.

UNDERSTANDING BEHAVIOR

Big Idea

Our family and cultural backgrounds influence the foods we eat.

Essential Questions

What food traditions do different cultures have?

Why do families and other groups have customs and rules about food and eating?

How do we learn about foods from others?

How have food traditions changed over time where we live?

Key Concepts

- Each culture has distinct patterns of behavior, usually practiced by most of the people who grow up in it. (AAAS Benchmark 7A/1)

- People can learn about others from direct experience, from the media, and from listening to other people talk about their work and their lives. People also sometimes imitate people—or characters—in the media. (AAAS Benchmark 7A/1)

- What is considered to be acceptable human behavior varies from culture to culture and from one time period to another. (AAAS Benchmark 7A/2)

- Human beings tend to repeat behaviors that feel good or have pleasant consequences and avoid behaviors that feel bad or have unpleasant consequences. (AAAS Benchmark 6D/4)

Sample Activities

- Read a book that describes a variety of foods and eating customs, such as *Let's Eat: What Children Eat Around the World* by Beatrice Hollyer. Have students choose one of the cultures described to study further.

- In the garden or in pots, grow plants typical to different cultures, and have students create identification tags for them.

- Examine the school lunch menu to find foods that come from various cultures.

- Explore how influences such as culture, religion, medical condition, and geography might affect food choices. Suggest an influence (such as "lives in the desert" or "is always in a rush" or "is a vegetarian"), and have students name a food that a person might or might not eat because of that influence.

- Peruse newspaper and magazine ads related to food. What points does each ad emphasize to sell the product (such as price, healthfulness, or taste)? What other techniques or messages do you notice (such as catchy slogans, humor, or guilt)?

- Help students create a questionnaire to find out friends' and family members' favorite foods, and then graph the results.

- Interview older family members about foods they ate as children or about what foods were and were not considered healthy then. How have foods changed?

- Create fictional restaurant menus that describe and illustrate typical foods eaten at various time periods in your state.

- Find out about table manners at an earlier time or in another culture. Why do cultures and families have rules about eating properly?

- Develop an ad campaign for an uncommon fruit or vegetable—such as kiwi or kohlrabi—to convince classmates or schoolmates to try it.

HEALTH

LIKE OTHER COMPLEX ORGANISMS, the human body is a system of cells grouped into organ systems that get energy and building materials from food. By exploring the nutrients that different foods provide, students come to the understanding that a healthful diet incorporates a variety of foods. They also gain a deeper appreciation of how food and lifestyle choices affect health.

MAINTAINING HEALTH

Big Idea

Food provides the energy and building materials our bodies need to grow, develop, and thrive.

Essential Questions

What is a healthy diet?

What nutrients do we need to keep healthy?

How do our nutritional needs change as we grow up?

How does exercise contribute to health?

Key Concepts

- Food provides energy and materials for growth and repair of body parts. (AAAS Benchmark 6E/1)

- Vitamins and minerals, present in small amounts in foods, are essential to keep everything working well. (AAAS Benchmark 6E/1)

- As people grow up, the amounts and kinds of food and exercise needed by the body may change. (AAAS Benchmark 6E/1)

- Making healthy food choices includes basing decisions upon nutrient content.

Sample Activities

- Examine the nutrients found in various foods using nutrient grab bags. Paste a picture of a food (such as a carrot) on the outside of a bag, and place inside it strips of paper on which are written the nutrients found in that food (such as "carbohydrates" or "vitamin A"). Have students guess and compare the nutrients in different foods.

- Categorize the ingredients of foods by whether they primarily help the body "go," "grow," or "glow." Carbohydrates and fats provide energy (go), proteins help the body build and repair cells (grow), and vitamins and minerals help regulate body functions (glow).

- Create vitamin and mineral labels for garden plants to help other students learn which plants are particularly high in specific vitamins and minerals.

- Prepare a salad bar with a wide variety of ingredients from the garden or brought in by students. Help students to make their own salads, pointing out that the more colorful the salad, the more nutrients it will contain.

- Test for the presence of starch (a carbohydrate) in foods using iodine, which turns black when starch is present. Try several different foods, such as bread, potato, milk, spaghetti, apple, banana, tofu, and so on.

- Invite your school's food service manager to talk with students about how school lunch menus are planned with nutrient content in mind.

- Develop a poster or chart that shows which parts of the body are used in different kinds of physical tasks.

- Interview parents and other family members to find out ways their diet and exercise needs have changed over time.

- Search for information about the diet, health, and exercise of early Native Americans, explorers, or settlers in your area. What did they do to stay healthy and strong?

- Using wire clothes hangers and shapes cut from colored poster paper, construct healthy lifestyle mobiles showing things students can do to maintain healthy bodies. Examples may be eating fresh fruits and vegetables, walking to school, or playing outside.

ENVIRONMENT

A FOOD CHAIN IS THE SEQUENCE OF LIVING THINGS
through which energy flows in an environment. Food chains always
begin with the sun and then a plant, which uses sunlight to make food,
and then may continue with an animal eating the plant. A food web is
made up of all the food chains in an ecosystem, and shows how the
plants and animals in that ecosystem are connected. Studying these
relationships helps students gain a deeper understanding of how their
food choices both affect and depend on other living things.

SUSTAINING LIFE

Big Idea

Food is made up of energy and matter that are passed from one organism to another.

Essential Questions

Where do living organisms get their food energy?

What is a food web and what are the different jobs in a food web?

In what ways do people depend on food webs to survive?

How do the decisions we make about food affect natural systems, including food webs?

Key Concepts

- Some source of "energy" is needed for all organisms to stay alive and grow. (AAAS Benchmark 5E/2)

- Almost all kinds of animals' food can be traced back to plants. (AAAS Benchmark 5E/1)

- One of the most general distinctions among organisms is between plants, which use sunlight to make their own food, and animals, which consume energy-rich foods. (AAAS Benchmark 5A/1)

- Over the whole earth, organisms are growing, dying, and decaying and new organisms are being produced by the old ones. (AAAS Benchmark 5E/3)

- Food chains and webs are ways to represent feeding relationships among organisms.

Sample Activities

- Make food chains starting with a food students ate for dinner. Did it come from a plant or an animal? Where did that plant or animal get its energy to live and grow? If it was an animal, continue tracing the food energy back until you get to a plant and the sun.
  For example: Sun→Corn→Chicken→Person.

- Read a book to learn more about food chains and food webs, such as *What Are Food Chains and Webs?* by Bobbie Kalman and Jacqueline Langille, or *Staying Alive: The Story of a Food Chain* by Jacqui Bailey.

- Look for things that are budding, blooming, fruiting, and dying in the garden. How are each of these stages connected to our food web?

- Search for evidence of the cycling of matter in the garden—from plants to food waste to compost and back to the garden. Introduce the terms *producers*, *consumers*, *detritivores*, and *decomposers*.

- Use owl pellets from a scientific supply house to investigate one animal's food chain. (Owls cannot digest the bones or fur of their prey, and they regurgitate these parts in compact pellets.) Dissect the pellets to find out how many different animals the owl ate.

- Choose a wild animal to research. Find out where this animal lives, what it eats, and how it gets its food. Draw a picture of this animal's food chain. What would happen if one of the members of the food chain disappeared?

- Research one food item on the school lunch menu. Where did it come from? How did it get to your school? What was its original source? How might a student's choice to eat it or not affect food webs?

6-8

FOOD

IN HUNTER-GATHERER SOCIETIES, people were able to get the food they needed to survive using only a few simple tools, such as spears, fishnets, or digging sticks. Today's food system is a complex process involving countless people, a multipart transportation system, and numerous different technologies. Exploring this process is important for understanding the effects of our food choices on our society, on our health, and on our environment.

PRODUCING FOOD

Big Idea

There are many ways in which humans have managed the landscape, controlled plant and animal characteristics, and used technology in order to raise crops and animals for food.

Essential Questions

How did ancient cultures acquire the food they needed?

In the past and in the present, what effects have raising plants and animals had on the natural environment?

How have people used selective breeding to increase the quality and quantity of food?

In what ways do decisions about agriculture influence people's health?

Key Concepts

- Early in human history, there was an agricultural revolution in which people changed from hunting and gathering to farming. This allowed changes in the division of labor and the development of new patterns of government. (AAAS Benchmark 8A/1)

- People control some characteristics of plants and animals they raise by selective breeding and by preserving varieties of seeds (old and new) to use if growing conditions change. (AAAS Benchmark 8A/2)

- In agriculture, as in all technologies, there are always trade-offs to be made. Getting food from many different places makes people less dependent on weather in any one place, yet more dependent on transportation and communication among far-flung markets. Specializing in one crop may risk disaster if changes in weather or increases in pest populations wipe out that crop. Also, the soil may be exhausted of some nutrient, which can be replenished by rotating the right crops. (AAAS Benchmark 8A/3)

- By eating locally grown and seasonal foods, we can minimize the resources needed to produce food.

Sample Activities

- Compare the foods of ancient cultures. What did people eat, and how did they obtain, transport, and prepare their food?

- Explore the transformation from hunting and gathering to farming societies, and examine how this change affected the social structure.

- Use on-line sources to examine and compare aerial photographs of your area from 10 or 20 or more years ago with today. What percentage of the land in each time period is devoted to agriculture? What other changes in land use do you see?

- Trace back to its source the journey of a specific food that students eat in the lunchroom. What technologies were needed at each step of the journey?

- Use hydroponics as an inexpensive and relatively fast way for students to monitor and control variables that contribute to plant growth and development, such as light or water. [From *Benchmarks for Science Literacy*, p. 185]

- Research a particular crop or farm product—such as apples, wheat, corn, potatoes, milk, or beef—to learn about its native origins. Find out which states are now the top producers of that product, and consider how environmental conditions and selective breeding have contributed to its success.

- Do a side-by-side comparison of heirloom and hybrid tomatoes (or corn), including taste, texture, color, nutritional value, and so on. What are the advantages and disadvantages of each? How does seed saving affect plant diversity of gardens and farms, and why might that be important?

- Prepare snacks made from the school garden or from locally grown food. Then, discuss the tradeoffs involved in eating only locally grown food (first defining "locally grown" for the purpose of your discussion).

- Look for news reports of how well particular crops grown in your area are doing in response to weather, pests, market demand, government policies, and the like. [From *Benchmarks for Science Literacy*, p. 185]

CULTURE

FOOD IS ESSENTIAL FOR OUR SURVIVAL, but it is also part of our cultural identity and a reflection of who we are. How cultures produce, market, prepare, and consume food changes over time. By looking at food and patterns of food consumption, students examine the many influences that affect cultures and explore changing cultural values and behaviors.

UNDERSTANDING BEHAVIOR

Big Idea

Cultures have distinctive food patterns and behaviors that can change due to a variety of influences.

Essential Questions

What can we learn about different cultures by studying their food and the ways they procure, prepare, eat, and dispose of it?

How do ideas, values, and behavior patterns spread within a culture and from one culture to another?

How have past and present technological changes (including transportation) brought changes in food choices, food production, and human behaviors related to food?

Key Concepts

- Each culture has distinctive patterns of behavior, usually practiced by most of the people who grow up in it. (AAAS Benchmark 7A/1)

- Within a large society there may be many groups, with distinctly different subcultures associated with region, ethnic origin, or social class. (AAAS Benchmark 7A/2)

- Although within any society there is usually broad general agreement on what behavior is unacceptable, the standards used to judge behavior vary for different settings and different subgroups, and they may change with time and different political and economic conditions. (AAAS Benchmark 7A/3)

- Technology, especially in transportation and communication, is increasingly important in spreading ideas, values, and behavior patterns within a society and among societies. New technology can change cultural values and social behavior. (AAAS Benchmark 7A/4)

Sample Activities

- Design a garden plot that reflects a certain culture. In the design, consider specific techniques for growing and harvesting food, and rituals associated with its production.

- Look at resources, such as *Hungry Planet: What the World Eats* by Peter Menzel and Faith D'Aluisio, to learn how family meals compare in different countries and cultures.

- Explore the effect that age or culture has on people's favorite foods. Conduct a survey asking about favorite foods and then analyze the results, looking for patterns.

- Prepare a dish or meal typical of a culture or time period your class is studying.

- Go on a scavenger hunt at your local grocery store to find food items that come from as many other countries as possible. For homework, make a list of food items in your kitchen at home that come from other countries.

- Invite an elder to talk to the class about the ways in which foods have changed over his or her lifetime. How have social, personal, or technological factors influenced these changes? Write a short story about how foods might be different 20 years from now.

- Examine media messages about food and body image that are directed to students' peer group. What characteristics of youth culture are evident in the messages?

- Explore the impacts on an ancient civilization when a new technology was introduced that changed food production, such as agriculture, irrigation, or transportation. What are the possible impacts today of new technologies, such as genetic modification or computers?

- Conduct a "dig" of buried artifacts that represent food in a particular culture. Students dig up the artifacts using small trowels, brushes, and other tools, and analyze them. Artifacts may include food containers, dishes, utensils, fruit pits, bones, and other food-related items.

- Research and map the movement of a particular food (such as chocolate, coffee, sugar, potato, or tomato), showing its source and its spread around the world.

HEALTH

WE ALL NEED FOOD TO SURVIVE, but the specific foods we choose to eat can greatly affect our health and well-being. In fact, diet is directly related to a number of diseases, including obesity, heart disease, diabetes, and cancer. By taking a close look at the foods they eat and their own personal behaviors, students gain tools for making choices that promote health and fitness.

MAINTAINING HEALTH

Big Idea

Individual bodies may have different specific requirements for health, but all people need good dietary habits, healthy personal behaviors, and a toxic-free environment for optimal health.

Essential Questions

What effects do food choices have on body composition and optimal health?

How do the amount and types of food and exercise needed for health vary among individuals?

How have changes in the ways that food is produced affected the nutrient content of the food we eat?

What behavior patterns and food choices affect the health of the human body and the health of the environment?

Key Concepts

- The amount of food energy (calories) a person requires varies with body weight, age, sex, activity level, and natural body efficiency. (AAAS Benchmark 6E/1)

- Toxic substances, some dietary habits, and some personal behavior may be bad for one's health. Some effects show up right away and others years later. Avoiding toxic substances, such as tobacco, and changing dietary habits increase the chances of living longer. (AAAS Benchmark 6E/2)

- The environment may contain dangerous levels of substances that are harmful to human beings. Therefore, the good health of individuals requires monitoring the soil, air, and water, and taking steps to keep them safe. (AAAS Benchmark 6E/5)

Sample Activities

- Practice reading nutrition facts labels. Compare serving sizes, servings per package, calories, fat, and nutrient contents of various foods. What information is not contained on food labels? How can we find that information?

- Have students keep logs of the foods they eat and the activities they do for a day, including sleeping, reading, and sitting in class. Then use a calorie chart to calculate how many calories they took in that day and how many they burned.

- Create graphs of the food and exercise requirements of humans at different stages of their lives—as babies, children, teenagers, young adults, and elders. How do needs for energy (calories), protein, and other nutrients change?

- Make a list of harmful behaviors and a list of healthful behaviors. Using the two lists, help students set realistic personal fitness goals and monitor progress toward meeting those goals. How can we avoid substances and behaviors that are bad for our health?

- Bring in pictures of processed food for which the source is not obvious, for example, ketchup (tomatoes), spaghetti noodles (wheat), and French fries (potatoes). Look up the nutrient content of each processed food, and compare it with that of its source.

- Choose a healthy recipe to prepare in class. How can we adapt our favorite recipes to make them healthier?

- Research ways that diet and exercise affect muscle tone, bone strength, the circulatory system, and the respiratory system. Create posters to show others what you learned.

- Find out how skipping breakfast affects learning, and develop a marketing campaign—with bumper stickers, announcements, or other means—to encourage students to eat a healthy breakfast.

- Visit a supermarket to find as many different forms as possible of a single food, such as corn (fresh, canned, frozen, in dry mixes, in frozen entrees, and so on). Compare at least three of these products in terms of price, nutrient content, packaging, and distance traveled from their source. How do food choices affect both human health and environmental health?

ENVIRONMENT

ORGANISMS ARE LINKED TO ONE ANOTHER by the food energy they need to live and reproduce. This need results in a continuous flow of energy through the organisms in an ecosystem—from the sun to food producers (plants) to food consumers (animals, fungi, and bacteria). By studying how plants use the sun's light to store energy as food, and then how that energy moves through an ecosystem, students gain a deeper understanding of why food is so important and how they depend on the environment to satisfy this critical need.

SUSTAINING LIFE

Big Idea

A constant influx of energy is required for organisms to sustain themselves.

Essential Questions

How do plants use energy from light to make sugars?

What happens to the energy when food is transferred from one organism to another?

In what ways do people depend on this flow of energy?

Key Concepts

- Food provides molecules that serve as fuel and building material for all organisms. (AAAS Benchmark 5E/1)

- Plants use the energy from light to make sugars from carbon dioxide and water. Organisms that eat plants break down the plant structures to produce the materials and energy they need to survive. Then they are consumed by other organisms. (AAAS Benchmark 5E/1)

- All organisms, including the human species, are part of and depend on two main interconnected global food webs. One includes

microscopic ocean plants, the animals that feed on them, and finally the animals that feed on those animals. The other web includes land plants, the animals that feed on them, and so forth.
(AAAS Benchmark 5A/5)

- Almost all food energy comes originally from sunlight.
  (AAAS Benchmark 5E/3)

- Over a long time, matter is transferred from one organism to another repeatedly and between organisms and their physical environment. As in all material systems, the total amount of matter remains constant, even though its form and location change. (AAAS Benchmark 5E/2)

Sample Activities

- Burn a peanut, cashew, or other nut to demonstrate firsthand the food energy stored by a plant. (*Warning:* **Do not do this if any student has a nut allergy.)** To do this, bend open one end of a paper clip, spear it into the nut, and place it on a metal pie tin. Then light the nut with a match, and time how long it stays lit.

- Model photosynthesis by having students hold cards labeled C (carbon), O (oxygen), or H (hydrogen) to form the 12 molecules on the left side of the photosynthesis equation, and then regrouping to form the right side:

6 CO_2 (carbon dioxide) + 6 H_2O (water) → $C_6H_{12}O_6$ (glucose) + 6 O_2 (oxygen gas). Point out that this process can take place only in the presence of sunlight, which provides the energy.

- In the garden or school yard, use pieces of aluminum foil to cover part of a leaf for a few days. Test the leaf for starch (a carbohydrate) by soaking it in rubbing alcohol for 2+ hours, and then placing an iodine solution over it. Where starch is present, the iodine will turn blue-black. What does this tell you about sunlight and plants?

- Take photos looking up into a canopy of trees, and study how the shape and orientation of the trees' branches and leaves maximize the sunlight they can capture.

- Look for evidence of food webs in the garden. How are people linked to these food webs?

- Investigate detritivores and decomposers in the garden. Describe their sources of food energy and the role they play in the food web.

- Weigh and graph the waste generated in the school lunchroom over the course of a week. What happens to this waste? Does any organism use it as a food source? In nature, what happens to food waste?

- Have students keep track of their food intake for a day, and use a calorie chart to calculate the number of calories they got from plant sources and the number from animal sources.

- Make a food web of a local ecosystem, such as a prairie, redwood forest, or tidepool. Each student researches one organism in the ecosystem—including humans—and writes on an index card where it lives, its food, and who eats it, along with a drawing of it. Post the cards and draw lines to show the food web connections.

- Simulate energy transfer in food chains with a relay race. Each team is made up of a producer, a primary consumer, a secondary consumer, and a decomposer. The producer starts with an armful of popcorn or leaves (energy), runs, and passes the energy to the next link of the food chain, and so on. Does all of the energy get passed through a food chain? Where does the rest of the energy go?

9-12

FOOD

IN ORDER TO FEED OURSELVES, our society depends on a complex food system with many interdependent elements. Plants, animals, weather, technologies, health effects, cultural biases, government regulations, world markets, and more play a part in this system. To make informed food choices, we must balance the influence and effects of these elements, and consider the side effects and trade-offs inherent in any food decision.

PRODUCING FOOD

Big Idea

Growing and producing food is a complex process that requires making trade-offs among such factors as economics, environmental costs and benefits, public health implications, animal welfare, and personal views.

Essential Questions

How have changes in food and agriculture affected people's lives—both today and in the past?

What side effects and trade-offs are involved with various agricultural and food production strategies in both local and world contexts?

How are selective breeding and the genetic modification of plant and animal species similar, and in what ways do they differ?

What role should economics, environmental costs and benefits, public health implications, and personal views play in decisions involving food and food production?

Key Concepts

- Agricultural technology requires trade-offs between increased production and environmental harm and between efficient production and social values. (AAAS Benchmark 8A/3)

- In the past century, agricultural technology led to a huge shift of population from farms to cities and a great change in how people live and work. (AAAS Benchmark 8A/3)

- Government sometimes intervenes in matching agricultural supply to demand in order to ensure a stable, high-quality, and inexpensive food supply. Regulations are often also designed to protect farmers from abrupt changes in farming conditions and from competition from other countries. (AAAS Benchmark 8A/2)

- New varieties of farm plants and animals have been engineered by manipulating their genetic instruction to produce new characteristics. (AAAS Benchmark 8A/1)

Sample Activities

- Explore the social and environmental impacts of the "Green Revolution" of the 1940s–1960s that led to significant increases in food production worldwide through the use of technologies such as irrigation, synthetic fertilizers, and pesticides.

- Read and analyze literature—such as John Steinbeck's *The Grapes of Wrath*—that shows how agriculture or food production has changed over the years. How have these changes affected people's lives and the environment?

- Participate in a volunteer or service-learning project at the local food bank or farmer's market, so that students can experience firsthand one part of our complex food system.

- Explore careers related to the food system, such as farmer, soil scientist, food scientist, veterinarian, biotechnologist, grocer, transportation engineer, and economist. What decision-making strategies does each employ?

- Investigate different varieties of a particular crop. For example, there are over 30,000 varieties of wheat in six different classes: hard red winter, hard red spring, soft red winter, durum, hard white, and soft white. What attributes of this crop have people altered through selective breeding, and what through genetic modification?

- Explore issues surrounding genetically modified foods. Elizabeth Marshall's *High-Tech Harvest: A Look at Genetically Engineered Foods* gives some insight into the techniques and issues. What are the benefits of modifying genes in our food plants, and what are the risks?

- Give students a hypothetical controversial situation to consider, such as the planned opening of a mega-dairy or meat processing plant in your area. Help them explore different positions on the roles economics, environmental costs and benefits, public health implications, and personal views should play in decisions involving food and food production.

- Search for and list as many different corn-based food ingredients and products as possible, such as high fructose corn syrup, dextrose, xanthan gum, and so on. How does the U.S. farm policy contribute to corn being "king"? What are the trade-offs—for farmers and for society—of being reliant on one crop?

- Research how farm policy drives decisions about what is grown or not grown in the United States.

CULTURE

PEOPLE IN ALL CULTURES EAT AND PREPARE FOOD,
and we all distinguish acceptable norms of behavior involving food.
However, cultures differ in how these traits are expressed. Often cultural
values and assumptions are so ingrained that the people growing up
in a culture may not even be aware of them. By examining this cultural
context, students become more aware of the ways that culture affects
the decisions that societies and communities make about food.

UNDERSTANDING BEHAVIOR

Big Idea

The decisions a society makes about food, food production, and food practices are influenced by the prevalent culture's values, assumptions, and norms.

Essential Questions

How might we uncover the ways that culture influences our own biases, perspectives, and beliefs about food and food-related behaviors?

How does our society's cost-benefit approach to decisions influence food and food practices, and how does that approach compare with the ways other societies make decisions?

What are examples of ways in which our society favors individual rights over the collective good as it relates to food? How do these examples compare with other societies' approaches?

Key Concepts

- Cultural beliefs strongly influence the values and behavior of the people who grow up in the culture, often without their being fully aware of it. (AAAS Benchmark 7A/1)

- Heredity, culture, and personal experience interact in shaping human behavior. (AAAS Benchmark 7A/4)

- Benefits and costs of proposed choices include consequences that are long-term as well as short-term, and indirect as well as direct…. But benefits and costs may be difficult to estimate. (AAAS Benchmark 7D/1)

- All social trade-offs pit personal benefit and rights of the individual, on one side, against the general social good, on the other. (AAAS Benchmark 7D/2 [Grades 6-8])

Sample Activities

- Make a list of dining behaviors, such as eating regularly, liking spicy food, sitting at a table, snacking between meals, using a fork, and so on. Categorize these behaviors as to whether they are universal (common to all people in all groups), cultural (common to a particular group), or personal (individual differences within a group). Discuss any disparities of opinion about the correct response.

- Conduct a cross-cultural simulation, such as Bafá Bafá (available from Simulation Training Systems, www.stsintl.com), that helps students examine their own cultural perceptions as members of two imaginary cultures.

- Many religions have rules about foods to be eaten or avoided, either at certain times or always. Select a major religion and design a pamphlet describing that religion's dietary rules and the reasons for them.

- Examine hereditary conditions that may influence cultural food preferences, such as lactose intolerance, allergies to wheat or nuts, or differences in metabolism due to gender.

- Invite your food service manager to talk to the class about how school lunch menus are decided. How are economic, social, and environmental factors included in the decision-making?

- Explore the idea of a 100-mile diet, in which you eat only foods that originate within a 100-mile radius of your home. How could you find what is grown or raised within that area? How would this diet affect your life or the environment? How would your diet compare with someone in another part of the country or the world?

- Take the Ecological Footprint Quiz (available on the Earth Day website, www.earthday.net), and compare your results with those in other countries. How does culture affect the size of one's footprint?

- Visit a local food bank or other food assistance agency to find out how the issue of hunger is addressed in our culture. What cultural values influence our actions and inactions about hunger? How do other countries respond to hunger?

- Debate the rights of individual farmers to use pesticides on their land versus the rights of farm workers employed on the land, the neighbors on adjacent properties, and the consumers who ultimately buy the produce. Look for examples in your local news of individual rights conflicting with each other or with a larger societal goal.

HEALTH

WITH RECENT TECHNOLOGICAL AND MEDICAL ADVANCES,
each of us has more tools for staying healthy than ever before in history.
Yet, paradoxically, food-related diseases, such as obesity and diabetes,
are on the rise and have reached epidemic levels in our country. How
can this be? Even when we aim to eat healthfully, other influences, such
as social environment, economic forces, media messages, and public
policies, can all work against our best intentions. By critically examining
these influences, we can strengthen our ability to make food choices
that contribute to our health and well-being.

MAINTAINING HEALTH

Big Idea

A variety of factors influence health decisions at both the personal and the societal level, including marketing, media messages, scientific information, public policy, personal preferences, and one's friends.

Essential Questions

Why doesn't everyone practice health-enhancing behaviors—such as eating healthfully—all the time?

How do public policies in our region or state promote human health?

What conditions in our society diminish human health?

Key Concepts

- New medical techniques, efficient health care delivery systems, improved sanitation, and a fuller understanding of the nature of disease give today's humans a better chance of staying healthy than their forebears had. (AAAS Benchmark 6E/3)

- Conditions now are very different from the conditions in which the species evolved. But some of the differences may not be good for human health. (AAAS Benchmark 6E/3)

Sample Activities

- Keep personal diaries of food intake and physical activities for a week. Analyze the factors that influenced whether or not you ate well or exercised on a given day.

- Develop a survey to learn how teenagers at your school decide what to eat for breakfast or lunch. Do they take into account cost, convenience, nutrition content, taste, advertising, friends' opinions, family expectations, or other factors?

- Choose a health-related food issue, and compare and evaluate different sources of information on that issue, including advertisements, food labels, and consumer advocate websites. How might each source of information help or hinder decision-making on that issue?

- Analyze school lunch menu items by rating them on a scale of 1 to 5 for nutritional value, with 1 being high-calorie, low-nutrition-value items (such as onion rings) and 5 being healthy whole foods (such as apples). If there are lower-value items on the menu, find out why and make recommendations to your school's food service manager based on your analysis.

- Watch the documentary *Super Size Me*. Discuss ways that American life leads to obesity, Type II diabetes, and other food-related health problems. What can individuals, organizations, and lawmakers do?

- Explore the history of food labeling and dietary guidelines in the United States. What have been the positive and negative impacts of these public policies?

- Hold a debate on whether schools should limit or eliminate access to vending machines in schools.

ENVIRONMENT

EVEN THOUGH MOST OF OUR FOOD TODAY comes from farms and ranches rather than from a natural environment, we could not produce food without the help of other organisms in the food web. Our food production practices and other activities also profoundly affect food web organisms and environmental quality. By helping students explore the ways their food choices both depend on and affect the environment, they can make better-informed and more responsible choices.

SUSTAINING LIFE

Big Idea

Human activities can affect the balance of food webs on which we vitally depend.

Essential Questions

How do geographical factors, such as climate, location of water resources, and mountains, affect the availability of food energy?

In what ways do human activities both depend on and affect food webs?

What does knowledge about the flow of matter and energy through living systems suggest for human beings?

Key Concepts

- The amount of life any environment can support is limited by the available energy, water, oxygen, and minerals, and by the ability of ecosystems to recycle the residue of dead organic materials. Human activities and technology can change the flow and reduce the fertility of the land. (AAAS Benchmark 5E/2)

- The chemical elements that make up the molecules of living things pass through food webs and are combined and recombined in different ways. At each link in a food web, some energy is stored in newly made structures, but much is dissipated into the environment as heat. Continual input of energy from sunlight keeps the process going. (AAAS Benchmark 5E/3)

- At times, environmental conditions are such that plants and marine organisms grow faster than decomposers can recycle them back to the environment. Layers of energy-rich organic material have been gradually turned into great coal beds and oil pools by the pressure of the overlying earth. By burning fossil fuels, people are passing most of the stored energy back into the environment as heat and releasing large amounts of carbon dioxide. (AAAS Benchmark 5E/1)

Sample Activities

- Design a garden habitat that uses local native plants to provide food for birds and other wildlife. Explain how these plants are suited to the physical features of the local ecosystem.

- Research how a decline in food and other resources contributed to the collapse of a civilization, such as the Roman Empire or the Anasazi. (See *Collapse: How Societies Choose to Fail or Succeed* by Jared Diamond for some historic and modern examples.) What can we learn from the fate of these civilizations?

- Learn about the dramatic decrease in honeybee populations in the United States in recent years. What are possible causes of this decrease? How might it affect food production? What are people doing about it?

- With the help of a local biologist or resource person, survey the macroinvertebrates in your local creek or river. (Macroinvertebrates are small organisms that are a vital link in aquatic food chains; because many are sensitive to pollution, their presence or absence can indicate the health of the water.) Find out how agriculture and other human activities may affect these organisms.

- Create slide shows or posters depicting the flow of energy and cycle of matter involved in fossil fuel creation and use, and the effects of that use today.

- Have students trace a food item from their favorite meal back to its original plant source, and research the impacts to the environment at each step of the food chain. At which steps are fossil fuels used for transportation or processing?

- Read *Animal, Vegetable, Miracle: A Year of Food Life* by Barbara Kingsolver et al., an account of one family's resolve to eat only locally grown food. Discuss what students would be willing to do to reduce the environmental effects of their food choices.

- Find out how land use rules in your state or region promote or limit development. How do these rules affect the food web in your area? What impact do they have on food production for humans?

- Discuss the fact that with over 850 million people in the world not getting enough to eat, many people believe any means is justified to produce the most food at the cheapest cost—no matter the environmental consequences. Have students write an essay about whether they agree, and why or why not.

Center for Ecoliteracy Seminars

The Center for Ecoliteracy has provided financial, intellectual, and practical support to hundreds of exemplary urban, rural, and suburban schools committed to organizing their curriculum and community around environmental learning. Based on lessons learned from networks of these schools, we have developed a series of seminars and professional development institutes that have been attended by educators from across the United States and abroad.

Center for Ecoliteracy Resources

Visual Guide: Linking Food, Culture, Health, and the Environment

We are facing a national health crisis, and much of the crisis is nutrition-related. What caused this? What influences our food choices? And is there a link between what we eat and socially and environmentally healthy communities? These are some of the questions explored in this 25-page guide to changing positive school lunch programs, developing an integrated curriculum, and establishing student goals that will help students make their way in the real world.

Rethinking School Lunch Guide

This 175-page on-line guide, developed with support from The California Endowment and the W.K. Kellogg Foundation, covers all aspects of developing a successful school lunch program, including procurement, waste management, curriculum integration, and financial viability.

Thinking Outside the Lunchbox Essays

A series of essays by Michael Ableman, Wendell Berry, Fritjof Capra, Marion Nestle, Michael Pollan, Alice Waters, and others on the connections between human and ecological communities and safe, fresh, and nourishing food, and the importance of rethinking your school lunch program.

Model Wellness Policy Guide

An on-line guide produced in collaboration with Slow Food USA and the Chez Panisse Foundation, which provides a process and language for crafting a wellness policy that addresses meal quality, physical education, and instruction connected to diet and health.

For more information about these and other resources,
visit **www.ecoliteracy.org**

The Center for Ecoliteracy

2528 San Pablo Avenue

Berkeley, California 94702 USA